We Don't Get To Ring The Bell

My CML Story

Dear Bunny & Richie —
Thank you for your support over the years!
Love,
Anne M McAuley Lopez

By Anne McAuley Lopez

LUPI DOCS & DESIGNS
Box 12343
Scottsdale, AZ 85267

We Don't Get to Ring The Bell, My CML Story

Anne McAuley Lopez
anne@agencycontentwriter.com
agencycontentwriter.com

Manufactured in the United States of America.
ISBN: 978-1-7339561-3-0 (print)

Cover Design: Copper Theory Creative
www.coppertheorycreative.com

CONTENTS

Dedication

To my husband, Eddie, for your never-ending love and support. I couldn't do this life without you and am grateful for you every day. You are my rock, and I love you.

To my Dad, Eddie and I couldn't have fought as hard as we have without your love and support. We are forever grateful for you.

To Jen, my BFF since first grade, I didn't mean to scare you when I was diagnosed. We're going to live a long, happy, Golden Girls life. I love you, my sister!

To my brothers Ed and Dan, and sister-in-law Jaime, I am sorry I didn't tell you more about how I was feeling in that first year post-diagnosis. I love you and love the memories we have created and will continue to create.

To my nephew and niece, I am blessed to be your aunt and am enjoying seeing you grow up! Thank you for the love and laughs.

To my Stepsons, you are handsome, smart, and brave. I am blessed to have you in my life. I meant what I said when I married your Dad, I may not have given birth to you, but you are mine at heart. Thank you for making me and Dad laugh!

Thank you, Stanley, our canine companion, for your dedication to protecting the family, making us laugh, and staying by my side when I am having a bad day.

Thank you to my first readers who helped craft the final version of the story. I appreciate your time, effort, and feedback.

To Team McLopez, you all hold a special place in my heart. You supported me when I didn't know I needed it. I appreciate you.

To my Sisters with Blisters, over the years our lives have changed and our experiences have shaped who we are and who we have become. Know that I hold each and every one of you near and dear to my heart. Our time together has meant the world to me.

To my friends from St. James School, your friendships, love, and support mean the world to me. I wear my, "I survived Catholic school so I know I can beat cancer" t-shirt proudly. Thank you for the many years of love and laughter!

To my oncologist and naturopathic teams, you saved my life. There are no other words.

For my mother, my mother-in-law, and to all that we have lost to cancer, thank you for being warriors. Thank you for your bravery.

To my CML brothers and sisters, I wrote this for all of us because we don't get to ring the bell. Stay strong and keep fighting. A cure is on the horizon.

To the researchers and patients in clinical trials, thank you for your dedication and bravery to finding a cure.

To my editor Christine, thank you for pushing me to places I didn't know I needed to go. Without you, this book wouldn't have happened.

To my graphic designer Caitlin Kelly who created the cover of this book. It is always a pleasure to work with you. Thank you for taking my ideas and making them a reality.

FOREWORD

by Eddie Lopez

I am the lucky and blessed guy who gets a front row seat to the life of Anne McAuley Lopez. I married my Queen Anne on March 13, 2016.

I will always cherish that moment, becoming husband and wife in front of family and friends. But we remember thinking something was *off* that day. When we look back, we now realize the signals were there. She was frequently exhausted. She had minor bruises on her arms for weeks that wouldn't go away. We figured it was the stress of wedding planning. At the time we would have never guessed....cancer.

I still marvel that when Anne's naturopathic doctor told us the news, that her white blood cell counts were at elevated levels and that it could be leukemia, we never felt despair. We never felt like our love, our marriage, or our lives would be threatened. We simply accepted it as a challenge we would face and overcome together.

Since that day I have lived with deep admiration for my beautiful bride. She sought out all the research and information she could find about managing and living with Chronic Myeloid Leukemia (CML). She found online support groups and connected with others living for many years with CML. She took control of her own healthcare. She trusted her instincts while ignoring those who tried to steer her to alternatives that we just knew would not be right for her. Everything she discovered was immensely helpful, but it took a lot of work to find it.

We wondered if everyone with CML felt this way: confused, hearing conflicting views, struggling to find clear answers, seeking support. At a time in your life when it feels like your foundation is shaken and you are facing new obstacles, it would be nice to know what to expect on your journey forward. It is reassuring to hear from others who have navigated all of this and found a path forward that works for them.

As I write this, my beautiful bride is approaching four years of undetectable leukemia. When she was first diagnosed, I wanted this more than I had wanted anything in my life: undetectable cancer. I would have moved mountains to help her get here. Now that she has been undetectable for so long, and maintained her quality of life, I never want to take a single moment for granted. From the outside, she does not look like she has leukemia. But I know the struggle she endures every day. I know the discipline she has to take her miracle pills every evening and manage the side effects. I see the frequent naps she has to take, even when she is frustrated because she is trying to get things done. She is not in remission, and right now she doesn't get to ring any bells. This is a fight that she will always have, and I commit to stand beside her through every moment of this fight—until the day a cure is found.

Overall, I feel an overwhelming sense of gratitude. I am grateful for the miracle pill that saves her life and lets me continue to love her on this Earth. I am grateful for the prayers of so many friends, family members and community members that help her through every day. I feel blessed for friends who understand when we have to cancel plans at the last minute because she is exhausted. I am thankful for managers and colleagues who have understood when I need to take time away from work to care for her. I marvel at the doctors and nurses who have researched her condition and provided her compassionate counsel and care.

She is the best person to write this book because she has lived it. She has not only faced the external obstacles in healthcare, cancer treatment, and insurance denials. She is unstoppable. When necessary, she has taken her story to the insurance companies, to the press, and even to Congress. She has overcome the internal obstacles as well, the uncertainty, the lack of control, the physical toll of nausea, pain and exhaustion. She has overcome them with the highest levels of grace and poise I have seen, and with reserves of strength and determination that continue to wow me.

She wrote this book because she wants to give you insights she worked hard to obtain, and she wants to offer you support. Most of all, she wants to give you hope. The same hope that keeps our family going every day. The hope that it is possible to have a high quality of life even with this condition and the necessary treatments. The hope that YOU can choose what is best for you and everyone will understand and everything will be okay. The hope that today's medical research continues to get us closer and closer to solving this, and someday there could be the cure we all seek.

For the caretakers like me, I hope you will draw hope and inspiration from my Queen Anne's story as well. We want you to know your support is more valuable to your own cancer warrior than you even know.

- May you know the joy of seeing improved cancer cell counts. It surprisingly becomes the most tangible means of measuring your quality of life.

- May you feel the sense of promise when you read about a new study that could possibly lead to a cure.

- May you know the feeling of being the rock and the source of strength for your cancer warrior, especially at the times when she or he needs you most.

- May you know the feeling of being just you and your cancer warrior—just you two—against cancer, against healthcare, against the system, against the world. May you appreciate what you have already overcome—together—and know that you can handle anything Life throws at you.

- May you, at your lowest moments, turn your struggles, worries and fears over to your friends, your family, your God or your higher power—and feel yourself uplifted with renewed strength.

- May you know what it is like to cancel plans with friends at the last minute, and instead of any disappointment you may expect, you feel their understanding and support. May this help you appreciate even more those days where you are able to enjoy plans with friends.

- May you witness the battle, the aches and pains, the nausea and exhaustion. May you feel their frustration. May you know the feeling of holding and comforting them through their low moments. And in return, may you feel the pride of seeing them at their best—knowing what they had to overcome to get there.

We wish for you the entire experience of loving and caring for someone special in their fight against CML.

With warmest wishes for you on your journey,

Eddie Lopez

Husband, Caretaker, Rock, Advisor,
Champion and Head Cheerleader for Queen Anne McAuley Lopez

INTRODUCTION

When cancer patients finish treatment, they ring a bell to signify they are done and ready to move forward cancer-free. As CML patients, we don't get to ring the bell. Many of us continue taking our chemo medication (TKI) daily because there is no other option and there isn't a cure...yet.

It is for this reason that I decided to write this book.

In July 2016, just four months after marrying my husband Eddie, I was diagnosed with Chronic Myeloid Leukemia. It brought our world to a halt. We didn't know where to turn for information and support, but eventually we found our way.

Through our local chapter of the Leukemia and Lymphoma Society, Families Raising Hope, and online groups, I met other CML patients, and began to understand the science of the condition, how to manage side effects of the medication, and I began to thrive again.

My CML brothers and sisters, you give me hope to continue fighting. You give me strength because I know I am not alone. You provide resources when I am too exhausted to research. You give me a reason to write this book.

As I've traveled along this path, I have heard stories from other CML patients who also struggle to find resources. We are a small but mighty group, so we rely on each other.

And we don't get to ring the bell.

We experience nausea, body aches, muscle and bone pain, and fatigue from the medication we take daily. Others experience heart and lung conditions as a result of the medication. And we keep fighting for our lives.

The purpose of writing this book is to share with you my experience as a CML patient.

Understanding that all of our paths are different, I want to give you all that I know, answering the most asked questions that I see in the online groups.

I want you to feel hopeful when you read this book.

I want you to feel light and love.

I want you to know that when I say I pray for you, that I really do pray for you.

You are stronger than you think and supported more than you understand.

I know I can't possibly cover everything about CML in this book, but I want you to know that I wrote it with you in mind. My hope is that you can feel a small sense of peace as you read, and an understanding of your diagnosis.

There is hope on the horizon with new medications being tested as I write. Keep fighting.

Yours,

Anne

THE DIAGNOSIS

LOOKING BACK

I've had my writing business since 2010 and for periods of the next six years, I had no insurance. In January 2016, I was eligible for domestic partner insurance through my then fiance Eddie's employer. We were getting married in March of that year so very quickly, my status would change from partner to wife. To get the ball rolling, I scheduled a well woman exam and a physical. The doctor required two separate appointments "for insurance reasons," so I scheduled the well woman appointment for January, and the physical in April.

At the time, it was important to get a well woman exam plus a mammogram. I admit I hadn't had either in a few years, and because my mother died at the age of 46 from breast cancer, I scheduled that appointment first. Thankfully, everything came back normal.

At the March 16, 2016 wedding, I noticed I was tired. My hair was falling out. Most noticeably, I had a bruise that wouldn't go away. I remember telling Eddie I needed to ask my naturopath which arnica salve I should use to heal the bruise faster. I kept forgetting. At the time, none of these factors immediately prompted me to see a doctor, and I knew I had the physical coming up in April, so I made a mental note to bring them up "just to see" what the doctor would say.

For all of my 40-something years, bloodwork had always come back normal. This time my cholesterol was elevated which wasn't all that surprising given our family history of heart issues. But what was odd was that my white cell count was elevated.

White cells are the ambulances of the blood, heading to injuries to heal and fight infections. Normal range is 3,000-10,000 while cells. In April, my white cells were 23,700. The PA I was seeing wasn't worried because, at the time, I felt asymptomatic, meaning I had no other symptoms of being sick. She suggested we wait a month or two and redo the bloodwork. It seemed, based on my medical history, to be an anomaly. Maybe I had an infection I was fighting. We weren't overly concerned at that time.

In June 2016 Eddie and I were in Connecticut for a vow renewal ceremony in the Catholic Church with our East coast friends and family. We were there for a week and every night I woke from my sleep with severe anxiety. It felt like an elephant was on my chest and I could hardly breathe. No matter what I did, the elephant wouldn't leave. I also noticed that I was more tired than usual but chalked it up to getting engaged, married, and vow renewal in the same 12 months, all while running a business.

Years earlier I had been on anti-anxiety medication and had taken myself off it. I strongly advise not doing this as it was against what my doctor had told me and what was recommended for the medication.

In 2016, I was under the care of my naturopath for anxiety, using natural remedies to control and treat. When I had the attacks while in Connecticut, I thought we simply had to change my treatment protocol, so I made an appointment.

While we did change the anxiety protocol, on the way out the door, I mentioned the blood work that I had back in April that had shown elevated white counts and cholesterol. I asked if we could do the bloodwork through the naturopath, who was acting as my primary care doctor at the time. She agreed. It was a Thursday. She said they'd only call if something was odd and seeing as my blood work had never been out of normal ranges, we weren't all that concerned.

On the following Monday, the naturopath's assistant called and said, "The doctor wants to see you tomorrow to review your bloodwork. Bring someone with you. Are you available at 9 or 10am?"

There was no negotiating the appointment time. There was no discussion. I selected a time and told Eddie what was happening with a splash of humor. I, like Chandler Bing on the classic TV sit-com Friends, handle stress with humor.

"The doctor wants to see me to review my bloodwork. I guess you have to bring a friend for high cholesterol now. You'll probably have to tell me to stop eating bad foods."

The words hardly matched the look on my face, or his. We knew something was wrong. Silence hung in the room like a heavy cloud. He hugged me and whispered that we would get through this, whatever it was, and that we shouldn't speculate.

Our dog Stanley's crate was next to our bed. I remember bracing myself on the kennel so I didn't fall over.

When we arrived at the doctor's office, we were ushered to a private room where my doctor had the blood work ready to review. We began discussing my high cholesterol which led to talk of eating grass fed beef because I needed more iron in my diet and then on to bruises that we had noticed on my legs.

I thought the bruising was because our dog was too rough when he played. Our dog Stanley was a puppy at the time and would not stay still. He regularly was jumping at me, and tromping all over me when sitted or laying down. Looking back, that was kind of ridiculous. It was obvious something else was happening.

Back then, every night Eddie would look at my legs for bruising before getting into bed. I didn't bump my leg on a dresser or door. No one was hurting me. When I awoke the next day, he'd look again, and there always were more bruises. On the way to the bloodwork review, we had decided to mention it to the doctor as it now seemed like a symptom of….something….we just weren't sure what yet.

The doctor then turned the lab report to us. In bright red ink my white count was 56,100 and CRITICAL.

My heart sank. What was happening? Was this even real?

The doctor referred me to an oncologist-hematologist who was expecting my call.

By Thursday of the same week, we were sitting in an oncologist's office, a place I never wanted to be given that my mother had died of cancer. I didn't know what my odds were, what the treatment would be, if any, and what would happen to my four month old marriage.

It was at this appointment that I met the oncologist and her nurse practitioner. They said that while something was happening and I needed additional blood work, they thought it could be treated with a pill. If anything was terribly worrisome, I'd already be in an ambulance on my way to the hospital to start chemo treatment. "Wait, what?" Yes, chemo. That meant one thing. Cancer.

My veins are small like my mother's and it is always easier to use a butterfly needle like they use for kids. The nurses seemed to think they could use a regular needle. It took three nurses trying about five times to get a vein that would bleed enough for about a dozen vials of blood of varying sizes. I was bruised, battered, and stressed.

The purpose of this round of bloodwork was to narrow down what was happening in my body. Was it an infection? Was it an autoimmune disease? It was neither of these. I had the BCR-ABL mutation which is the telltale marker for Chronic Myeloid Leukemia.

Two days after the bloodwork, on July 26, 2016, one month to the day after our vow renewal, we were back at the hematologist oncologist's office meeting with the nurse practitioner. She confirmed the diagnosis of CML, and shared the treatment–a pill. I'd need bloodwork two weeks after starting the pill and then monthly for the foreseeable future. No one said "Cancer," but it was confirmed. I had it.

THERE IS NO CURE BUT IT IS TREATABLE

At the time of diagnosis, my BCR-ABL was 86% meaning 86% of my cells had the mutation, and my white cells had grown to 58,200 from 56,000 in just a week.

The growth of the white cells meant they were crowding out the red cells. Red cells bring oxygen to the body. Without fully functioning red cells, I was feeling fatigued and had brain fog.

Eventually, without treatment, I'd likely be at the hospital complaining of being out of breath because of the lack of oxygen. Thankfully, we caught my leukemia relatively early.

After two weeks on Gleevec, the chemo pill, my BCR-ABL dropped to 78% and continued to drop over time. That meant the pill was working and my immune system was resetting. Over time, the bruising became less which was a small, welcome, and reassuring change.

We reconnected with the naturopath once we had the CML diagnosis and asked if there was anything she could do to help. When we arrived, we were again ushered into her office. This time her husband, who is also a naturopath, was there too. They each have their specialties and I was such a special case, I needed them both. He recommended high dose Vitamin C infusions.

Because I had vitamin infusions at the naturopath's office prior to my CML diagnosis, he asked if I wanted to explore getting a port placed. It would not only make infusions simpler, we could use it for blood draws.

We'd already met our insurance deductible so we moved ahead with the port placement. The hospital required that I have bloodwork done. That was August 2016 and my white cell count had nearly doubled to 111,000. That was the highest it was ever tested.

In addition to taking Gleevec daily, Tuesdays and Thursdays were spent at the naturopath's office for four hours each day. I received more Vitamin C than you can take orally. It acts as hydrogen peroxide to essentially clean the blood. It doesn't touch the healthy cells and kills the cancer cells. We were supporting my immune system in massive ways.

As we moved ahead with infusions, he gave me time to talk about how I was feeling emotionally and physically. Together we utilized natural solutions to manage the side effects of the chemo pill – from bone and muscle pain to severe nausea, headaches, brain fog, and nearly all of the side effects listed on the prescription insert. It was a long twelve months.

We managed side effects week-to-week, sometimes day to day (more on this in a later chapter). The naturopathic team worked with the oncology team, which is rare, and we made sure nothing interfered with Gleevec. The chemo pill was the most powerful defense and the rest was to support the immune system. My BCR-ABL had been on a downward trajectory for months but had stabilized with counts below 1%.

While a significant milestone that some patients never reach, I am a perfectionist, and we wanted my immune system to work just a bit harder. Prior to this diagnosis, I rarely would get sick so I knew my body had the potential to reach the ultimate goal.

After 13 months of rigorous treatment, we received the news that my leukemia was UNDETECTABLE!!

We were cautiously optimistic but then it upticked slightly a short time later, but still below 1%, and I was disappointed. Working with my medical team, we changed my naturopathic protocol, working on eating non-inflammatory foods so my body could focus on supporting my immune system. Within a few months, my leukemia was once again undetectable and has remained such for three years and counting.

To this day, I have a naturopath and hematologist oncologist that I see quarterly. I still have the port because blood draws from my veins are traumatic and I continue to get vitamin infusions, though now maybe only monthly.

To say I am grateful, is an understatement. I couldn't have gotten to where I am without the support of my husband, medical team, and an army of people around the globe praying for me.

When my blood counts had clearly stabilized and were improving, I asked my nurse practitioner to be honest with me.

I said to her, "We're conservative with my treatment because my CML grows fast, aren't we? We caught this in time, didn't we?"

With tears in her eyes, she looked directly at me and nodded. I am a breathing, walking, miracle warrior. This is my CML story.

How Has CML
Impacted My Life?

How has CML impacted my life? That is such a loaded question. Honestly, in many ways it has enriched my life. I know that sounds crazy to say cancer has enriched my life but for me, it has.

I've grown closer to my husband Eddie, Dad, brothers Dan and Ed, family, and friends more than ever. I've been more open about talking about big topics like my feelings, palliative care, big pharma, and the financial cost of cancer. I've reached out for help from people and organizations more than ever. I've said YES more...and NO whole lot more. I've learned that my health is my number one priority which means my part-time job, my writing business, weekend plans, and travel all take a back seat to rest and renewal. If I want to be active, I have to make time to rest.

I say that as if it was a magical switch that flipped in my head but that was not the case. I tend to be stubborn as the day is long. It took a lot of convincing for me to see the reality of my diagnosis and the need to take care of my mind, body, and spirit over all else. The first year was tough on many levels.

Throughout the journey, I've called my dad after every appointment. In the beginning, I think I called him after blood draws, which are really a non-news event. It's the bloodwork report that's important but that didn't matter. However old I am, my dad wants to know how his little girl is, so we call. Even now, five years into diagnosis and three years with undetectable leukemia, I call my dad after every appointment with my oncologist. At this point, I think I am just superstitious that if I stop, the news will be different.

I distinctly remember calling my dad from the car after the appointment with my naturopath where we learned my white counts had skyrocketed. We were waiting for an appointment to be made with the oncologist. Eddie was driving and we had pulled into a parking spot in front of the Thai restaurant by the doctor's office. I remember silence as if the air had been sucked out of the room. Then the barrage of questions from my dad, none of which we could answer until I went to the oncologist.

The air came back once we learned more about the diagnosis and treatment for CML. My dad was at our house the first night I took my chemo pill, Gleevec. It was mid-August 2016.

THE FIRST YEAR

Gleevec, the TKI medication I take, is often referred to as the miracle pill because it changed the course for CML patients. Prior to Gleevec, CML was a terminal illness, giving patients 2-3 years life expectancy after diagnosis at most. Now it is manageable, and the majority of patients live normal life expectancies. That doesn't come without a cost.

When I received my first Gleevec prescription, I read the lengthy insert. I was thinking that on other medications, I don't experience side effects, so this one wouldn't be different, but I was wrong. Within the first year, I had at least muted versions of many of the side effects listed:

- Fatigue

- Bone Pain

- Muscle Pain

- Headaches

- Brain Fog

- Nausea

- Low Iron

- Thinning Hair

- Slow Regrowth of Hair and Nails

- Rashes/Skin Irritations

While the oncologist prescribed anti-nausea medications, the rest was left to my naturopathic team. Advocating for myself, I've chosen to work primarily with the naturopathic team to manage side effects. They've been miracle workers in finding ways to manage the side effects of the TKI. Thankfully, I haven't had to change TKIs, so we've been able to keep that constant. Some patients have to change TKIs because their bodies aren't responding, but that comes with its own set of side effects of which I am not familiar. Your Healthcare team can give you more information on that.

In the beginning, post-diagnosis, as my body got used to Gleevec, we navigated side effect management. The bone pain was bad. I felt years older than my age for a period of time, months, maybe a year. I was slow getting into and out of the car. I walked slower. I wore comfortable shoes whenever possible. It was exhausting.

There was one night that the pain was so bad I prayed for God to take me. It was in this moment of pain that I understood why patients want a right to die. The pain is just too much to handle. It's all I could think about and focus on. To say I was thankful to wake the next day, is true. I also knew that we needed a new way of managing the pain. It wasn't soon after that we navigated getting a medical marijuana card. I take an edible every night and have never had another thought of wanting to die from the pain.

Under the constant care of my oncology and naturopathic teams, I take prescription, medical grade natural supplements. These supplements, like an adrenal supplement to combat fatigue, signal my body to do what it knows how to do. Without it, my body is slow to respond or is non-responsive. Other supplements include Vitamin B-complex, Probiotic, Magnesium Orotate, and a mushroom complex. We're not simply treating symptoms; we are addressing the root of what is happening.

- Adrenals and B-complex for energy.

- Probiotic for GI issues.

- Magnesium Orotate for anxiety and muscle relaxation.

- Mushroom complex to support the immune system.

Please consult with your oncologist and physician before taking any supplements. Make sure whatever you're taking isn't interfering with your TKI. Advocate for yourself and ask your doctors if you're not sure.

This is important, to ask your doctors, before taking anything, even if it isn't to treat a CML-related issue. I heard a story of a CML patient who was depressed taking a common natural antidepressant without doctor's supervision. Turns out the supplement blocked their TKI from working, causing her BCR-ABL count to increase. Once they told the oncologist what they were taking, the oncologist knew the supplement was the likely culprit of the change to the blood counts. I tell you this story as a cautionary tale told to me by an oncology nurse. Always let your doctors know what you're taking.

Rather than going the natural route to treat my own anxiety and depression, I asked my general practitioner to prescribe a pharmaceutical that wouldn't conflict with my TKI. I have heard in online CML groups that others suffer from depression. And who wouldn't? The reality is that we live with incurable cancer every single day.

We don't finish treatment and get to ring the bell. That's our reality.

When I think about that for too long, it makes me angry and sad and I want to punch things. So I don't…very often…think about that reality because it's counterproductive and this is life. Instead I prefer to focus on:

- the beautiful life my husband and I have created.

- my family and friends.

- my nephew and niece who are beautiful and fun.

- my stepsons who are all smart and handsome, each with their own bright personalities.

- walking my dog on a sunny day, breathing deeply, recognizing the beauty God provides, even through our darkest days.

You may want to make your own list of things to focus on and refer to it regularly or when you need an injection of positivity. For me, I had to come to this realization. It wasn't always like this (remember when I shared a bit ago how thinking about incurable cancer for too long makes me feel?).

CHANGE OF MINDSET

For the first few months post-diagnosis, I was focused on *killing cancer cells*.

It wasn't until my naturopath said, "I know you're a writer so this is weird to say to you. I want you to use different words when you talk about your cancer. Instead of saying you're killing cancer cells, say that you're *supporting your immune system*. Let's see what happens."

I can't begin to thank her enough for this simple message. I hadn't thought about it like that. My mindset shifted almost immediately. I wasn't focused on the cancer from that point forward, I focused on ME, as a person, again. Here's my mantra:

- I am a warrior.

- I have a strong if a bit broken, immune system that needs to be supported.

- I flex my arms in the mirror.

- I hold my head a little higher.

- I am writing again.

- I am not as focused on the CML, I am focused on being myself.

- I feel better. My mental health is better.

- I am able to not think about cancer every day.

The best part is that I shifted from thinking of myself as a cancer patient to someone who has a chronic illness. When I began to think of this journey as a chronic illness, I gave myself permission to slow down, to say no, and to also say yes to what I want to do and where I want to spend time. It has been a game changer.

THE SPOON THEORY

I am not as energetic as I used to be. Years ago, when I started my writing business, I was able to write for hours on end, focusing on research and writing. Then I could go out with friends or stay up late watching television. I understand I am older than I was back then and that plays a role but my energy was sapped when I started my TKI.

I, quite unscientifically, describe it as my body focusing on keeping the leukemia in check so there is less energy for other functions. In addition to having significantly less energy, especially in the first year post-diagnosis, my hair thinned and nails grew slowly. My skin would get dry more easily than it had in the past and my body ached like I was much older than I am. It was depressing.

Before CML, my body was an efficient machine. I rarely got sick. When I did, I needed to sleep for a day or two and then felt better. I could exercise and see results. I was a night owl. I also didn't understand other people with chronic illnesses. Now I have a much better idea because I am one of them.

A friend told me that instead of having a full plate of activities, to have a half a plate. That way when I am tired, I have time to rest and if I have energy, I have time to do more. To that end, I set reasonable expectations of when and how much I can write in a single writing session. I write in the morning or late afternoon because that's when I have the most energy. There are rarely hours-long writing marathons. When I write for hours at a time, I am usually exhausted the next day.

I understand that my energy is finite, much less than what it used to be, so I need to carefully manage it. In the chronic illness world, some of us call ourselves 'Spoonies.' The term comes from an article called "The Spoon Theory" by Christine Miserandino (refer to Sources), where she values her personal energy as a certain number of spoons each day. Each activity she does "costs" a certain number of spoons and once she runs out, that's all she can do for the day; her body needs rest.

If I have a specific number of spoons for each day, you might think I am limited but I am not. I simply have to figure out how many spoons I need to accomplish what I want any particular day. Most days I work and then rest or nap, especially if I have plans, that evening. Other days I have boundless energy and can take on multiple tasks like writing and household chores, or take the dog on a longer walk. It just depends on what my body wants to do.

When I was first diagnosed with CML, I was working from home on my writing business, which was a blessing. Everything I did took more than one spoon. If I was up for four hours, I'd need to sleep for four hours. My body was getting used to the chemo pill and my immune system was essentially rebuilding itself, fixing the broken cells while still keeping me alive and functioning. I had to lean into fatigue to get to where I am today.

On my worst days, I had to nap after only waking and taking a shower. That was beyond frustrating. I hoped for so much more, and about nine months later, I found I had more energy. I needed less naps during the day and when I did need a nap, it wasn't a four hour event. That's when I knew I was on the right path.

Every milestone I've hit, like not needing to nap four hours a day, I thought would be the best I would feel, but I've been surprised many times.

The Warrior Inside

When I was first diagnosed, I wrote a blog post where I shared, "My inner warrior is tired. She needs to rest." It wasn't until I was reviewing it with my book editor Christine that I realized a shift of my mindset. Honestly, it was Christine who noticed it first. Am I a warrior? Is the warrior a different part of me? Am I a Survivor? I had to ponder this for weeks because it was a web of emotions.

Being a survivor, to me, means I beat cancer. I am out of the woods. I don't take medication or need chemo treatments. To me, it means I got to ring the bell and that will never happen. I get jealous of patients who get to ring the bell. They are, at least in that moment, free of more treatments, free of chronic pain, free of nausea and vomiting.

I am survivING because my CML is undetectable. That is only because I take a chemo pill everyday. Survivors are my Sister with Blisters teammate who overcame breast cancer TWICE and now has a clean bill of health. That's not me.

I am a fighter, a warrior. My body fights leukemia every single day. My mind knows I have an incurable cancer and yet my soul allows me to see the beauty in the world.

I describe it as this. You get a cold and it lasts three days; when I get a cold it lasts a week. That's because my immune system is always working, more than other people's systems are. I am a warrior because my body is fighting every single day to keep me healthy.

I fully recognize the Survivors face their own path to recovery. I am not by any means making their path any less because mine is longer term. I've seen many people ring the bell who continue to fight, some even losing their battle. As time has passed, I get it. I too am a Survivor...but I don't get to ring the bell.

I am a CML warrior and so are my CML brothers and sisters. And yes, I am a Survivor. Though I prefer to say survivING. The patients who participated in the first clinical trials for TKIs are warriors. The patients that are in current clinical trials for a new TKI called Asciminib are warriors (see Sources).

The warriors I cannot thank enough are the caregivers.

WHERE I AM TODAY

I think when I referred to my inner warrior, it was me not quite ready to accept the new life that I have now, as a cancer warrior. As time has passed, I've married the ideas of the old me, pre-CML, and the CML me now. It has taken a few iterations of creating the new me, in the new life.

Let's take it back a few steps.

There's the fact that I had gotten married four months before I was diagnosed. I became a wife and stepmom, then a cancer patient within months.

I had spent 40+ years as unmarried me, as a McAuley, as a writer, and since I was 22 years old, as a motherless daughter. It was profoundly life changing to become Mrs. Lopez. I was struggling with changing my name. Was I Anne Lopez? She sounded like a Spanish teacher – *Hola, Senora Lopez!* It wasn't quite the right fit. Was I keeping McAuley as my sole last name? I respected my husband too much to not take his name. Hyphens are kind of 1980's so McAuley-Lopez wasn't quite right.

After about a year, maybe two, I legally changed my name to what I had changed it to on Facebook on my wedding day – Anne Marie McAuley Lopez.

I am called Mrs. Lopez and I love it.

I am Anne McAuley Lopez.

I am a cancer patient.

And I am Aunt Anne.

My nephew was born eight months after I was diagnosed. While I was getting back to feeling good, I wasn't ready to travel cross country. In fact, I didn't meet him until the weekend of his first birthday. On that trip, I realized that I could travel, as long as I planned for rest. That trip was a win on many levels.

I trusted my body would be okay if I listened when I needed to rest.

I wore a mask on my flights.

I needed to be physically surrounded by the love of my family.

Being an aunt meant more to me than I ever thought it would.

My brothers and sister-in-law needed to see me, to see that I was okay. We needed to talk about CML and my journey. It was as healing for me as it was for my family and friends.

One year later, I became an aunt again. I met my beautiful niece when she was just three weeks old. We've had lots of time together with her brother, (uncle) Eddie, and me.

I am blessed beyond measure.

In Sickness and In Health

I don't know where I would be without Eddie's love and support. Through this time, I have been afforded opportunities that I don't think I would have without him. On my worst days, he lets me rest and orders in whatever food I am craving at the time. Eating is a challenge some days because of nausea and headaches. On my best days, we enjoy wine and cheese tastings, time with family and friends, and sunset walks in the neighborhood. He never pushes me, always supports me.

I remember looking him in the eyes and saying, "This isn't what you signed up for. You can leave. I will move back east where my family can support me more closely."

Without taking a breath, he said, "We are in this together. This isn't what either of us signed up for and I will not leave you. I support you no matter what. If we needed to move somewhere else for a clinical trial or treatment, I would move heaven and Earth to do that for you."

That's a new level of the vows I didn't expect, or I guess I hadn't really considered the gravity of it: *for better or worse, in sickness and in health.* This is our life together. Eddie has been at my oncology appointments and reminds me nightly to take my chemo pill. He holds my hair back when I am throwing up and rubs my back when the body aches are too much to handle. He plans dream vacations and understands I need time to rest along the way. He is my rock. In many ways, he too is a warrior.

What I've learned is that everyone is a warrior in one way or another. The friends with migraines are warriors. The friend fighting cancer is a warrior. The ones who rang the bell are warriors.

We have to wake up each day and be who we are.

I Have More Empathy

I have more empathy for people who need a little extra help. One of the biggest lessons I learned going through my CML experience is that when I don't feel well enough to take care of household chores, for example, everything is still there when I am ready. Nothing is earth shattering. I used to think if the house wasn't clean and the dishes weren't done that I needed to make that a priority above other things. Now I understand the value of using my limited energy to spend time with loved ones, to say yes to a wine tasting event or dinner with friends, instead of folding laundry. I feel a bit silly telling you that cancer was what made me realize this, but it is true.

It's okay to need help from our caregivers, friends, and family, even strangers:

- We've hired people to clean our house.

- We have groceries delivered or ready for pick up.

- We've hired a dog sitter and asked friends to walk Stanley.

- We do whatever makes life easier for me and for our family.

On my worst days, at the beginning of my CML journey, I spent way too much time worrying about things that I realize now are not all that important. Even if it was a bit late, the bills got paid, the dog got walked, and my clients extended grace to me.

I've also learned to extend grace to other people. I understand more about why my friends who get migraines would stay home and nurse themselves back to health or why my doctor with Rheumatoid Arthritis would not schedule her first appointments until 10 o'clock in the morning. Sometimes our bodies need time to adjust to medication.

Our bodies need time to get out of bed. We need our naps and slow days. Streaming services and DVRs were made for people with chronic illness. We need our resting time so that we can have time out of the house. I didn't understand that until I was diagnosed with CML.

When I am feeling my best, and sometimes even when I am not, I smile, even under my mask, and people appreciate good energy. And smiling makes me feel better too.

OUR FIRST TRIP

By October of 2017, Eddie and I had not taken a honeymoon. In the months before we planned to take that long-awaited trip of an escape to Kauai for a weeklong adventure (including a seven-hour flight), we decided it would be prudent to first fly a couple hours to Portland, Oregon for a long weekend. Baby steps.

As a precaution and to give my immune system a fighting chance (pun intended), I wore a mask on our flights and while on a bus tour. I can't imagine going on a bus packed with strangers now, but this was well before Coronavirus. We planned for resting time and were able to spend our days walking through the city tasting baked goods and coffee, visiting the Columbia Outfitters flagship store, and enjoying the laid back Portland vibe. We drove to the beaches and visited Roloff Farms with a friend and her family on the first weekend of pumpkin season.

If you're not familiar with Roloff Farms, it is the home to the Roloff family, and the stage for their reality television show. I've watched their family grow up and expand to include in-laws and grandchildren. It was a hoot to experience what I had previously only seen on television. My husband and I even got a photo with the oldest son and a conversation about how soccer is an important part of their culture in that part of the country. It was a rainy, fun-filled day. And not once did I think about CML.

PORTLAND WAS A VICTORY

Thinking back to that trip makes me a bit teary because it was the first time in many months when cancer wasn't the main focus. That's not to say it is our sole focus but quite often our friends ask how I am doing and what my counts are. I am more than open about talking about it, and at the same time crave conversation about anything else. That trip was a victory.

I finally felt like the months I had spent since diagnosis getting used to the medication and side effects were somewhat under control. I had an idea of how far I could push my body; as it turned out, I could push farther than I thought. It was around this time that my mantra *mind over matter* began.

When it was, and still is, challenging to get out of bed, I ask if it is a mind over matter issue or is my body really too tired. Many days it is a mind over matter issue for me. To combat this, I lean into my love of coffee and set the brew timer for an hour when I know I need to be up and running. The smell of coffee often motivates me,and the scent can help me get moving. Of course, there is also our dog Stanley who is my charge on many days.

NEW RULE: TAKE THAT TRIP YOU WANT TO TAKE

We took our honeymoon to Kauai in November 2018. If Portland was a trial run to see how far I could push my body, then Kauai was our real first trip together as man and wife, to a place neither of us had experienced. If you've never been to Kauai, I encourage you to visit. It's heaven on earth.

We took a redeye flight so that we could sleep. I looked ridiculous with my face and eye masks, but I was able to sleep. We arrived at happy hour time, stocked up on groceries, and headed to the resort, in awe of the beauty of the island along the way.

The trip was magical. We spent a day on a boat. Kauai is more beautiful, if that's even possible, from the ocean. We snorkeled with sea turtles and brightly colored fish. We drove around Waimea Canyon and tasted chocolate at Princeville Botanical Gardens. We saw a rainbow on the remembrance of my mother's birthday, November 29th. We attended a private dinner and luau. It was a dream vacation and we headed back to Kauai in June 2021 (while I was on a break after writing the first draft of this book) for another visit to heaven on Earth.

That's what you do when you have cancer. You enjoy all that life has to offer.

THE DOG EFFECT

We were given a seven-week old Stanley in June 2015, when Eddie was just my boyfriend. Eddie and I were engaged in September of that year and got married March 13, 2016. I love having dogs and included a vow that I could keep any furry creatures I brought home. While I've threatened a hundred times to get another dog, Stanley is our only dog. He is a terrier mix and I think fares better as our sole companion.

Originally, I wanted a dog so that I would be encouraged to be more active. Walking is great exercise. At the time we got him, we lived in a house with a yard. On my worst pain days, he would just be let outside whenever he asked. I taught him to ring a bell near the door to tell us he wanted outside.

Terriers are more demanding than the Labrador mixes I've had before. They're smart, almost too smart. In fact, Stanley knows that when he rings the bell, I get up, so he runs to the bell and rings it. I get up and before I can barely step, he runs to the snack closet! That little stinker has me up and down like it's my job, which from his point of view, I guess it is. Now that we've moved to a condo, Stanley and I take a couple of walks a day. And it has been good for both of us.

My husband Eddie often joins us on our walks. He was out of work for a number of months during the Pandemic in 2020 and received his call for a job offer while we were out for a walk! He laughed a bit and had to admit he would need to sprint home to get to his pen and paper to write down the specifics of their offer. While most walks are not nearly that entertaining, it is the support of Eddie and our companion Stanley that has helped me through a large part of my CML journey.

MAKE TIME FOR WHAT'S IMPORTANT

Since my diagnosis, I've realized the importance of seeing family and friends, of making memories that will last a lifetime, no matter how long that lifetime is, and the importance of taking in each and every moment. When I hug you, I really mean it. When I ask how you are, I really mean it. And when I say YES, it is because my mind, body, and soul are all in.

SOURCES

The following printed materials were mentioned in this Chapter, and some additional resources (used with permission where possible, for reference only).

"The Spoon Theory" by Christine Miserandino
https://butyoudontlooksick.com/articles/written-by-christine/the-spoon-theory/

On the Horizon: Asciminib, a New Drug for Treating R/R CML - https://www.medscape.com/viewarticle/942607

WHAT DO WE KNOW ABOUT CML?

What we know about CML is as interesting as the cancer itself. It was discovered in 1959 but effective treatments weren't available until the first clinical trials in the 1990's. What happened in those decades? In a nutshell, there was a stop/start of research happening and technology advanced to the point that TKIs were developed. The learning continues to this day.

WHERE IT STARTED

In 1953 James Watson and Francis Crick published their discovery of DNA in the scientific journal Nature. In 1956 it was confirmed that human DNA contains 46 chromosomes in 23 pairs, with one set inherited from each parent. In 1959, researchers discovered the genetic cause of Down Syndrome, an extra chromosome.

I mention Down Syndrome because it is a topic near and dear to my heart. My mother's sister Jackie had Down Syndrome and my mother advocated for her and others like her for her entire life. If you've never met someone with Down Syndrome, I encourage you to do so. They are the most loving people you will ever meet.

In 1956, a young scientist named David Hungerford was working at a Philadelphia cancer research center. As he looked through his microscope, he saw unusual looking cells. They were starfish-shaped cells of a drosophila fly. He was likely one of only a few in the world to see abnormally shaped cells at this time. That same year, a doctor named Peter Nowell, was working at the University of Pennsylvania. Nowell accidentally discovered a new method for looking at the chromosomes inside cells while looking at the blood from leukemia patients. Because the genetics community was so small at the time, the two began working together.

In 1959, just three years after they met, Nowell and Hungerford discovered an abnormality in the chromosomes of CML patients. Hungerford, an avid photographer, snapped a photo of what they saw. The shortened chromosome would come to be known as the Philadelphia chromosome, the telltale mutation for CML patients, and the photo would represent the starting point for developing targeted chemo therapies.

THE 1970'S RESEARCH AND DEVELOPMENT

While Nowell and Hungerford continued their research, there was nothing more significant discovered for nearly a decade. The 1970's brought new technology and interest in understanding DNA, chromosomes, and cancer. In 1972, just one year before I was born, Janet D. Rowley was studying the shortened Philadelphia chromosome. It was thought that it was one mutation that caused a shortened chromosome, but Rowley discovered the mutation was actually a translocation of Chromosome 22 and Chromosome 9.

The translocation is a spontaneous mutation meaning it happens after birth and is therefore not an inherited condition, only genetic, meaning it happens at a genetic or chromosome level. In other words, CML patients cannot pass the condition along to their children, or at least that is the current research.

According to the International Chronic Myeloid Leukemia Foundation (iCMLf), in 1980, Professor John Goodman from Imperial College in London, was the first to use stem cell treatment for CML. He also pioneered the use of unrelated donors with transplants and developed the PCR technology for monitoring CML. In 1997, he also confirmed the pre-clinical efficacy of the first TKI, STI571 now called Gleevec/ Imatinib and was a part of the development of second generation TKIs. You can learn more about him by checking out his profile on the International CML Foundation website (see Sources).

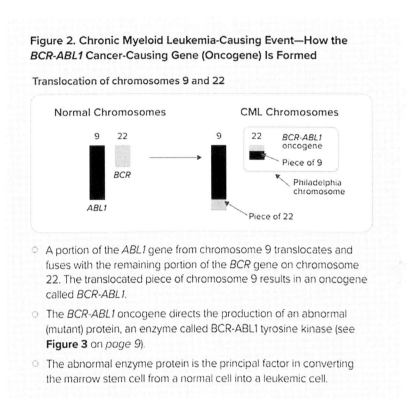

Figure 2. Chronic Myeloid Leukemia-Causing Event—How the *BCR-ABL1* Cancer-Causing Gene (Oncogene) Is Formed

○ A portion of the *ABL1* gene from chromosome 9 translocates and fuses with the remaining portion of the *BCR* gene on chromosome 22. The translocated piece of chromosome 9 results in an oncogene called *BCR-ABL1*.

○ The *BCR-ABL1* oncogene directs the production of an abnormal (mutant) protein, an enzyme called BCR-ABL1 tyrosine kinase (see **Figure 3** on *page 9*).

○ The abnormal enzyme protein is the principal factor in converting the marrow stem cell from a normal cell into a leukemic cell.

Image used with permission of The Leukemia & Lymphoma Society (CML, page 6, Revised 2020, see Sources)

DR. BRIAN DRUKER

There are many more researchers studying CML and other cancers as a result of the work of these scientists and doctors. The most notable I have found is Dr. Brian Druker who has dedicated his life to how CML works and not just how it can be managed, but also toward finding a cure. I consider him one of my personal heroes.

While much has been written by and about Dr. Druker, the best story I've come across is from the May 2011 issue of Smithsonian Magazine, a portion of which I've included here:

> *CML is one of the four main types of adult leukemia, but it is not common, striking 5,000 people in the United States each year. As a rule, it is fatal, with most patients dying within five years of being diagnosed. The first phase, a stealthy explosion of otherwise normal white blood cells, can last months or years; patients are often alerted to the condition by a routine blood test. If the disease goes unchecked, the white cells become increasingly abnormal, issuing helter-skelter from particular stem cells in bone marrow called myeloid cells; such leukocytes burst capillaries, overwhelm organs and suffocate tissues by crowding out oxygen-carrying red blood cells. The disease's course is exceptionally predictable, physicians say, but its clockwork nature has also provided scientists with an opportunity: prying into the molecular gears and springs that propel CML, they understand it better than any other cancer... .*
>
> *Brian Druker arrived at OHSU in 1993, years before the tram would be built and the hall-of-fame mural in the adjacent passageway would include a picture of him. Tall, as lanky and light footed as a greyhound, soft-spoken, Druker was 38 and had just spent nine years at the Dana-Farber Cancer Institute, part of Harvard Medical School, in Boston. "I saw cancer as being a tractable problem," he recalled of the research path he chose after finishing medical school at the University of California, San Diego. "People were beginning to get some hints and*

*some clues and it just seemed to me that in my lifetime it
was likely to yield to science and discovery."*

At Dana-Farber, Druker landed in a laboratory studying how a normal
human cell gives rise to runaway growth—malignancy. Among other
things, the lab focused on enzymes, proteins that change other mole-
cules by breaking them down (gut enzymes, for example, help digest
food) or linking them up (hair follicle enzymes construct silky keratin
fibers). Enzymes also figure in chain reactions, with one enzyme acti-
vating another and so on, until some complex cellular feat is accom-
plished; thus a cell can control a process such as growth or division
by initiating a single reaction, like tipping the first domino. Under the
lab's chief, Thomas Roberts, Druker mastered numerous techniques for
tracking and measuring enzymes in tissue samples, eventually turning
to one implicated in CML.

Working out the details of why this particular enzyme is the key to
CML had involved hundreds of scientists around the world—research
that would lead to several Nobel Prizes—but here's basically where
Druker started:

> *"First, all CML patients have the renegade enzyme in
> their white blood cells.*
>
> *Second, the enzyme itself is the product of a freakish gene,
> called BCR-ABL, formed during a single myeloid stem
> cell's division and thereafter transmitted to billions of
> descendants: the tips of two chromosomes, those spindly
> structures that store DNA, actually swap places, causing
> separated genes called BCR and ABL to fuse (see illustra-
> tion). The new mutant BCR-ABL gene sits on a peculiar
> chromosome discovered in 1960 by scientists at the Uni-
> versity of Pennsylvania. This 'Philadelphia chromosome,'
> visible through a microscope, is CML's hallmark.*
>
> *Third, the BCR-ABL enzyme is the evil twin of a normal*

enzyme that helps control the production of white blood cells. But like a switch stuck in the 'on' position, the mutant spurs the wild proliferation that is leukemia.

You didn't have to be a Harvard doctor to see that a single enzyme that causes fatal leukemia was, as researchers say, an attractive target for intervention. And indeed, scientists were then setting out to find or invent compounds that could block the BCR-ABL enzyme."

That blocking agent became the TKIs used to treat CML today.

Over the years, I've met other CML patients, including receiving a call from a patient who was in the initial clinical trials at UCLA, working with Dr. Druker's research partner.

Virginia's Story

One day, soon after my diagnosis, my phone rang and the woman said, "You don't know me personally, but we have a friend in common. My name is Virginia Garner, and I was patient number 15 in the initial clinical trials for Gleevec."

Turns out Virginia knows a friend of one of my Sisters with Blisters (see **Who is Your Support System?**). Small world.

I had goosebumps. I sat down and listened as she told her story.

She had been on a waiting list for a transplant. She had failed out of all other available treatment at the time and had to choose between a transplant and a clinical trial. Her doctor told her there was a clinical trial that she could try. She had to decide. She chose the clinical trial.

I thanked her for her bravery. She was among the first patients to take Gleevec. She was a pioneer. One day there will be an opportunity for me to participate in a clinical trial and I hope I can be as brave as Virginia and the other patients who went before me. If not for their decision, many of us would have different stories to tell.

THE BREAKTHROUGH

On May 28, 2001, the Time Magazine cover was a picture of pills with the headline, "There is new ammunition in the war against cancer. These are bullets. Revolutionary new pills like Gleevec combat cancer by targeting only the diseased cells. Is this the breakthrough we've been waiting for?" (see Sources)

For CML patients, it was indeed the breakthrough we needed.

The use of targeted chemo pills to treat other cancers is a bit more common now. Researchers and organizations like the Leukemia and Lymphoma Society (LLS), share what they learn about blood cancer with researchers of other cancers.

In 2016, Eddie and I were invited to an LLS cocktail party with the National Board of Directors, including LLS President and CEO Dr. Lou DeGennaro. It was an honor and a pleasure to simply be invited. What we heard made us more passionate about supporting CML researchers and patients.

A gentleman got up to speak. He wasn't wearing a suit and was clearly not a professional public speaker. He was a man who loved his wife. He shared their story, beginning by telling us she had breast cancer.

The room got quiet. We looked at each other thinking he was in the wrong room. This was a blood cancer event.

He continued on to tell us that his wife is alive and breast cancer free because blood cancer researchers shared what they learned. This information was shared with breast cancer researchers and together they created a treatment for breast cancer.

Goosebumps again.

My mother died from breast cancer in 1995. If the money we were fundraising for blood cancer could save me as well as save other children from losing their mothers to breast cancer, then this was where Eddie and I needed to be.

From 2016 to 2019, Team McLopez, with the help of friends and family across the country, raised $40,000 at LLS Light the Night for blood cancer research. In 2017, I was asked to be the Honored Hero (see Sources). I told my CML story at venues across the Phoenix area, including in front of the 7,000+ participants of Light the Night. In 2019, I was asked to share my story at the American Cancer Society's Relay for Life.

What's Next for CML?

Since the development of Imatinib/Gleevec, the first line treatment, there have been second line drugs developed. These include Dasatinib/Sprycel, Nilotinib/Tasigna, Bosutinib/Bosulif, and Ponatinib/Iclusig. The effectiveness of these drugs is measured in a PCR blood test to measure the BCR-ABL cells.

For the first three years, I was tested monthly, for BCR-ABL, and other blood counts. Because my numbers have been stable, I am now able to go every quarter for bloodwork.

The goal is to first stop the growth of cancer cells. Then to stabilize blood counts, eventually getting them to normal. They also monitor the spleen as it can become enlarged when the immune system is overworked.

Information vs. Misinformation

There is a lot of information and misinformation about CML that I see online in CML social media groups. Dr. Kendra Sweet of Moffitt Cancer Center in Tampa, FL studies leukemia and in particular, CML.

In her presentation for patients that was hosted by LLS, she busts three myths about CML that I think are worth mentioning here (see Sources).

1. **Myth:** I must get to undetectable and if I don't, I am failing treatment.

    Actual: The primary goal in the chronic phase of CML is to prevent progression to an advanced phase of CML. There is no need to be undetectable to prevent progression. In fact, according to Dr. Sweet, the majority of patients may never reach undetectable and they do well long-term.

2. **Myth:** If I miss a couple doses of my TKI in a month, it is not significant.

    Actual: According to Dr. Sweet, data suggests that there is a significant decrease in the number of patients achieving Deep Molecular Responses when adherence to treatment is less than 90%. That means taking the TKI at the same time everyday is highly important. I've taken mine between 6:30 and 8:30 every night since August 16, 2016, with a few variations based on travel or dinner time.

3. **Myth:** I must remain on my TKI forever.

    Actual: There is Treatment-Free Remission (TFR) available for patients who meet a certain criteria (I will cover this in the TFR Chapter).

Overall, with TKI drugs of any generation, there is hope for managing the growth of cancer cells, living a long and happy life, and hope for a cure. I firmly believe there will be a cure in my lifetime. When I asked my Oncology Nurse Practitioner, she said it is quite likely with the pace of research and the sharing of findings.

UCLA Research

In October 2019, UCLA Newsroom published an article titled, "Antibody Eradicates Leukemia Stem Cells" (see Sources).

They stated, in part the following:

> *"The introduction of the drug imatinib in 2001 revolutionized the treatment of a type of cancer called chronic myelogenous leukemia. In more than 80% of people with CML who received the drug, the disease went into complete remission.*
>
> *However, in most people with chronic myelogenous leukemia, cancerous stem cells remain in the body for years after their cancer has gone into remission. If treatment with imatinib or another similar medication is stopped — and in some cases, even while treatment continues — the leukemia stem cells can cause cancer to recur.*
>
> *Now, in experiments in mice as well as isolated human cancer cells, UCLA researchers have discovered a way to eliminate the CML stem cells. Their approach uses an antibody to block a protein that the stem cells rely on to grow. The advance, described in a study published in the Journal of Clinical Investigation, might eventually help treat not only chronic myelogenous leukemia but other cancers as well."*

This is exciting news for CML patients. In another chapter, I write about Treatment Free Remission (TFR) which is when a patient works with their oncologist to taper down their TKI. Eventually, they will cease taking the drug and closely monitor their blood counts, including BCR-ABL. Studies indicate there is about a 50% failure rate and patients end up back on their TKI. The reason is what is cited in the

UCLA article – CML patients relapse because they still have CML stem cells. The antibody that kills the stem cells, would effectively be a cure. It is quite promising.

SOURCES

The following printed materials were mentioned in this Chapter, and some additional resources (used with permission where possible, for reference only).

CML Foundation - www.cml-foundation.org

Crick and Watson - https://en.wikipedia.org/wiki/Molecular_Structure_of_Nucleic_Acids:_A_Structure_for_Deoxyribose_Nucleic_Acid

David Hungerford - https://www.cmleukemia.com/dr-david-hungerford.html and https://www.oncolink.org/cancers/leukemia/chronic-myelogenous-leukemia-cml/the-philadelphia-chromosome

Experimental Hematology and Oncology - https://ehoonline.biomedcentral.com/articles/10.1186/s40164-020-00170-6

Honored Hero - https://www.facebook.com/annemcauleylopez/posts/10212655332999822

John Goldman - https://www.cml-foundation.org/about-icmlf/executive-structure/33-john-goldman)

Leukemia Lymphoma Society - CML Booklet, Revised 2020 https://www.lls.org/booklet/chronic-myeloid-leukemia

Peter Nowell - https://www.pnas.org/content/114/18/4569

The Philadelphia Chromosome (https://www.amazon.com/Philadelphia-Chromosome-Improbable-Invention-Lifesaving/dp/1615191976)

Relay for Life - https://www.facebook.com/annemcauleylopez/posts/10218928688509789

Dr. Sweet - https://www.lls.org/sites/default/files/National/USA/Pdf/
Slides_Transcipts/transcript_cml_9.25.19.pdf

Time Magazine, May 28, 2001 - http://content.time.com/time/cov-
ers/0,16641,20010528,00.html and http://content.time.com/time/
subscriber/article/0,33009,999978,00.html

Types of Treatment - https://www.cancer.net/cancer-types/leukemia-chron-
ic-myeloid-cml/types-treatment

UCLA Research - https://newsroom.ucla.edu/releases/antibody-eradi-
cates-leukemia-stem-cells
https://www.jci.org/articles/view/129061
https://www.genengnews.com/news/new-path-for-preventing-chron-
ic-myelogenous-leukemia-relapse-discovered/
https://www.smithsonianmag.com/science-nature/a-triumph-in-the-
war-against-cancer-1784705/?no-ist

Virginia Garner - http://www.cnn.com/HEALTH/9910/25/leukemia.drug/
https://www.amazon.com/Journey-Finish-Line-Surviving-Together/
dp/0692864431
https://www.youtube.com/watch?v=BmewswCG6aM

June 2016 Just before diagnosis Eddie, Me, My Dad

March 13, 2016 Wedding Antique Wedding House Mesa Arizona Sunset

Fall 2016 St James
School Friends sent this
shirt post-diagnosis

2017 Light the Night Honored Hero

October 2017 Portland Oregon

November 2018 Kauai Beach at Hanalei

November 2018 Kauai Honeymoon

November 2018 Kauai Sunrise Cruise

Spring 2018 My first solo trip   Christmas 2019 Rockefeller Center NYC
to CT after diagnosis

Summer 2020 Sedona Fearless in the Red Rocks

June 2021 Kauai

Spring 2021 Flying Solo

Spring 2021 Writing and Stanley

Summer 2021 Idaho Falls

How Do You Choose Medical Professionals?

Choosing medical professionals in your CML journey can be challenging. For me, I didn't feel well. I would take a shower and then need to take a nap. I'd be awake for four hours and need a four hour nap. It was a trying time. Immediately, we embraced the naturopathic team and oncology team, especially because they were willing to work together on my behalf. That's uncommon and I am grateful that we had, and continue to have, a stellar medical team.

That didn't come without hiccups in the process. My original naturopaths moved out of state so I had to establish a relationship with a new naturopathic doctor. I needed mental health addressed; I've had anxiety and depression for many years. I needed a family physician. And all along the way I connected with other CML patients. I figured that as long as I needed others, they needed me too.

I'll write more about the friends and family who've supported me and Eddie in a different chapter. However, it is worth mentioning here because other CML patients can be resources for connecting you to the medical professionals you need.

Let's start with the most immediate need – finding a cancer doctor.

What's the Difference Between an Oncologist and a Hematologist?

I am prefacing this with a disclaimer that I am not a medical professional and that this is from my own experience and the experiences of my peers.

An oncologist is a general cancer doctor. They may see patients with varying types of cancer. Because CML isn't widely diagnosed, with only 15% of all leukemia cases being CML, according to the American Cancer Society, there are many parts of the United States, and the world, where there are no CML Specialists. Finding the best doctor that is close to you can be challenging.

An oncologist may be the best option but a hematologist oncologist, if available, may be a better option, with the best, of course, being a CML Specialist.

I currently live in the Phoenix, Arizona area. While we are one of the largest metropolitan areas in the country, there is no CML specialist covered by my insurance. I see a hematologist oncologist that my naturopath referred me to when I was initially seeking a diagnosis. While the doctor sees patients with different types of cancer, my nurse practitioner is focused on blood cancer. She reads the research about CML, understands TKIs, and has other CML patients, all of which are important for my care.

For a few months, I left my doctor to see another one. I'll call him New-Onc. New-Onc was not a specialist per se but seemed like he had clinical knowledge and interest. The problem was that he wasn't focused on me as a whole person, solely on how effective the TKI was. He didn't listen when I asked about side effect management (I go into this more in a different Chapter), only to interrupt me and say that if I didn't like the side effects, we could change drugs.

With only five drugs to choose at that time, I was floored to hear that for no clinical reason, New-Onc would switch my medication. Not only that but the side effect of the new medication would be heart problems and require EKGs on a regular basis. There are heart issues in my family so taking a chance with my heart for the sake of side effects didn't seem like a good idea for me.

The straw that broke me from New-Onc was when he told me that he wouldn't renew my medical marijuana card. He works solely with cancer patients at a cancer hospital and wouldn't let me get my second biggest tool for managing my CML – medical marijuana.

I returned to my original doctor and nurse practitioner.

My nurse practitioner renewed my medical marijuana card and encouraged it for pain management, including severe nausea.

A few lessons I have learned:

- The lesson I learned is that I am in control of my care.

- The lesson for you is to advocate for yourself.

- Find the doctors that are right for YOU.

- Ask the questions for which you want answers. Expect answers that make you feel that you are getting proper care.

- When you're looking for a doctor to manage your care, don't be afraid to visit a few so that you can evaluate who is the best fit for you.

BESIDES AN ONCOLOGIST, WHO DO YOU NEED ON YOUR TEAM?

Because my path to diagnosis was through my naturopath, I asked them to be part of my team. They accepted contingent on me seeing the hematologist oncologist, taking my TKI as prescribed, and most importantly, if I needed different care, like a naturopath who specializes in oncology, that I would be released from their care. They dug into research about CML. They researched natural ways to manage pain. They made us feel like we were part of their family and for that we are forever grateful.

We began a course of high dose Vitamin C infusions along with a laundry list of supplements. Supporting my immune system was, and continues to be, key to managing CML and the side effects of Gleevec.

Because I am not a doctor, I recommend seeking your own care guided by your chosen medical professionals and am only providing general supplements and not specifics.

- Immune support

- Adrenal support

- Vitamin supplements

- Natural pain management

- Anti-inflammatory foods

We tried a few supplements before finding the best ones for me. Because I had been seeing a naturopath for years before my CML diagnosis, I understood these solutions take time. As long as they listened to me, and continued to treat me, I felt positive about our outcomes.

Addressing Mental Health

As my body responded to the TKI and the leukemia inched closer to being undetectable, it became clear that I needed to manage my mental health. Crying in the shower and staying in bed for entire days wasn't healthy, at least not at the frequency it was happening. Cancer support groups were designed more for those in traditional drip chemo protocols. CML is an outlier and much of our experience is different so for me, groups weren't an option. That isn't to say they wouldn't be helpful for you. You have to find what works best for YOU.

I was depressed and not happy in my own skin.

When your body doesn't work after it has been darn near perfect for 40+ years, it is beyond frustrating. I questioned myself. Was the pain real? How much was I in control of managing the pain? Why wouldn't the brain fog clear? When would I be able to walk the dog and not be in pain? When could I eat dinner and take my TKI without feeling severe nausea? It was a tough time mentally and physically.

Eventually, I asked for a referral to a family doctor. I saw his Physician Assistant and was honest with her about how I was feeling – anxious and depressed.

I had managed my anxiety naturopathically for years, but my original naturopathic team had recently moved. Over the years we had become friends and if not for them doing bloodwork when they did, I may not be here today. To say their move rocked my world, is accurate. I cried when they told me.

On top of the CML-related issues, old feelings of depression returned, so there I was talking to the PA. I explained that years ago I was on a pharmaceutical anti-anxiety medication that managed my anxiety but overall made me feel emotionless. Eventually, defying doctor's orders, I stopped taking the medication. I should have worked with the doctor to wean, and I didn't and really should have checked myself into a hospital. This time, I didn't want to feel like I had no emotions, but I needed the rollercoaster of emotions to stop.

She found a medication to try for a period of time. It should help the anxiety and depression without interacting with the TKI. We set frequent appointments for med checks and to make sure my mood was improving, which it was. We ended up bumping the dose up just a bit, leaving room for one more dosage increase.

We also talked about the tools I already have to help me.

- 30 minutes of exercise on most days increases the happy hormones
- Walking is a great way to exercise and get sunshine.
- Writing my feelings.
- Focusing on what I can control.
- Weighted blanket
- Music at bedtime
- Eye mask when sleeping
- Mantras to say to myself when I feel anxious.

The last tip came from a call with a life coach who was in a networking group with me. I was telling her about challenges I was having in certain circumstances. I added the mantra to questions I would already ask myself when I have anxiety:

1. Where am I?
2. Am I safe?

3. What can I control at this moment?

4. Then I added, "They are doing what is best for them and I am doing what is best for me."

I used the last one when I was in a crowd and people were acting in a way that made me anxious. The combination of medication and what I call my toolbox, got me on a positive track. I was less anxious. The depression became manageable and then it was gone.

None of this happened over a short time, more like over months and even a year. It took understanding and support from my husband and determination from myself and my CML community.

I connected with CML patients in social media groups. I read their stories and shared mine. We shared tips for motivating ourselves and different ways of eating to control physical and mental well-being. This is what I found worked for me:

- Anti-inflammatory foods reduce my physical pain.

- Limited caffeine and processed sugar manage anxiety.

- Exercise fights depression.

- Petting my dog is good for my soul.

My food guidance is from my current naturopath. She is primarily managing my hormones and weight. Over the years, I've seemingly gained weight overnight. Now that my bloodwork has been stable over a period of time, we're able to look at hormones to see how they are impacting how I feel. We've added to the daily supplements and put more tools in the toolbox.

You Can't Manage CML Alone

There comes a time when you need to reach out to medical professionals for help and that is okay. If one professional isn't working for you, it's okay to seek another opinion. If you're not sure if what you're feeling is CML related, check in with the CML community groups on social media and seek medical attention. Advocate for yourself.

Side Effect Management and Palliative Care

Palliative care, as defined by WebMD, has "its own distinct mission: to relieve suffering and improve quality of life for people with serious illnesses" (See Sources).

That includes CML patients.

If you've ever read the insert of a prescription drug, you will see a list of side effects. I've never seen a longer list than the one in my TKI, Gleevec. The most common side effects include:

- Fluid retention (holding water)
- Muscle cramps, pain, or bone pain
- Abdominal pain
- Anorexia (loss of appetite)
- Vomiting
- Diarrhea
- Decreased hemoglobin (decrease in blood cells which carry oxygen)
- Hemorrhage (abnormal bleeding)
- Nausea
- Fatigue
- Rash

Managing side effects is a big part of everyday life.

Over the years, I have experienced many of these side effects including muscle and bone pain, severe nausea, diarrhea, fatigue, and brain fog. We've learned how to navigate these, and I've learned how to listen to my body with near-military precision.

TAKE YOUR MEDS ON TIME. ALL. THE. TIME.

Within two weeks of taking Imatinib, my BCR-ABL went from 76% to 18%. While I truly believe I am a miracle, I also know that I have been militaristic in taking my daily medication. With few exceptions, I've taken my medicine within the same two hours 1,700+ nights in a row and most nights within the same two-hour window. It's exhausting and frustrating especially when I'd rather be enjoying time with friends and family. I've thrown temper tantrums and threatened not to take it. Every time my husband is with me to hold my hand, rub my back, and on the worst nights, hold my hair as I dry heave.

I have a prescription for anti-nausea medicine which I take when we are out for special occasions. It constipates me so marijuana edibles are my preferred go-to when I am at home. Taking the pill with food, including carbohydrates, is the best way I have found to combat stomach issues.

Two of the best parts of this experience are that I have learned to listen to my body and advocate for myself as a patient. There are subtle effects like my lips getting dry and cracked or my hair texture changing that I have tracked and mentioned to my medical team. When my hair is growing, my nails often slow growth, and vice versa. When my immune system is working like a near-normal system, my lips are smooth. My hips and knees hurt less when I am exercising more but too much exercise will wear me out to the point that I need to rest. It's a delicate balance that takes effort. And I have to listen to what my body is telling me.

There are days when I feel like a superhero. I forget about the CML and the fatigue. I don't have pain or nausea. That's when I get A LOT done at home and at work. Other days I work for part of the day, take a nap, and take care of home tasks. And still others are a full day of rest. On a recent trip, I noticed my body wasn't adjusting well to the three hour time difference, so I went back to bed for a few hours. I awoke more rested and while it was later in the day, I was able to accomplish a few tasks.

It can be easy to get frustrated about what my body can and cannot do. I need more sleep some days than others. I need more water or electrolytes some days. The heat of an Arizona summer can be near-crippling, so I find ways to be active indoors and limit my time outside. I rest before we have an event or dinner with friends. It took me a while, but I am finally at the place where I call it a new-normal. Being angry about what amounts to a chronic illness isn't going to help and the stress will do more harm than good, so I take it day by day, week by week.

Over the years, I've talked to other CML patients as well as other people with chronic illness or watched YouTube videos to see what others do. While there are always folks who wallow in self-pity, I am not one of them. I see this as a new way to live and a lesson to be learned. I see my life as a tremendous gift. Without TKIs and my amazing medical team, I would not be here to tell my story. I would quite literally be dead now. Every single day is an opportunity to learn and grow; even on the worst days, I try to connect with people, even if it's just bringing my husband a cup of coffee while he works in his home office.

While I've always advocated for myself, a lesson I learned from my mother, I have become even stronger at communicating my needs. This includes what I want and also what I don't want in terms of my expectations from my doctors and specialty pharmacy. Ask yourself questions like:

- What do I like most about a doctor?

- Do I desire a level of autonomy regarding medical decisions?

- Am I able to advocate for myself or do I need someone to advocate on my behalf?

My mother was diagnosed with breast cancer in 1993 only after she demanded doctors continue to find a reason she was experiencing "unusual pain" in her breast. She knew what she usually felt, and something wasn't right. She wasn't a doctor and she needed someone to help her find answers. She sought second and maybe even third opinions about her pain. They found nothing on her mammogram, so they did an ultrasound. At the time, ultrasound wasn't used regularly to detect breast cancer but thankfully is now.

She ended up being one of the first patients to receive an MRI at a major university hospital in Connecticut, where I grew up. She joked that when she arrived for her appointment, they were just unwrapping the machine and had to learn how to use it before they ran her test. Based on the timeframe, I'd say that was darn close to the truth! MRIs were new and not widely used at the time. When the results came back, her doctor was able to confirm that she had Stage 3B breast cancer. If she hadn't advocated for herself, she may have never known what was happening in her body. Sadly, at the age of 46 and just 22 months later, she passed away.

When I think about the patients who have paved the way for me to have what is essentially a normal life with a chronic illness rather than dying from cancer, I consider my mother a pioneer. Her advocacy and being one of the first breast MRI patients was revolutionary. I'd venture to say her team learned from her case and no doubt were able to help someone else because of her.

As I was beginning my CML journey, my husband Eddie and I talked a lot about the kind of care I wanted and needed from my doctors. When I was new to Phoenix in the late 1990's, I needed a gynecologist. I didn't even know where to start in finding one, but I knew I wanted one who would allow me to ask a lot of questions and would find answers for me. Not all doctors, gynecologists or not, take the time with their patients. It's a sad and disappointing part of American medicine.

I went to my friend who had just had a baby and asked her about her doctor. She told me he allowed her to ask questions and was good with patient care. He became my doctor for many years because of his level of care that outweighed other factors, like having a man versus a woman gynecologist. Understanding what I needed helped tremendously in finding the right providers for me.

When I meet a new doctor, I tell them that I am a "reasonably compliant patient" which means that I take what they say seriously because they are the professional while at the same time, I listen to my body. Sometimes that means having a conversation with a provider about what is best for me, not just what is best per a traditional or most-used protocol. Throughout this journey, Eddie and I have talked about the importance of managing cancer as well as palliative care. I want the best quality of life, whatever that looks like for me.

As I began taking the daily chemo pill, I had severe nausea to the point that I would dry heave. My oncology nurse practitioner prescribed an anti-nausea medication which I take on occasion to this day. It causes constipation so I'd prefer to use edibles, but the edibles take longer to take effect and when the nausea is bad, it's easier to figure out constipation the next day than sit grabbing my stomach for any length of time. Lots of water and electrolytes help with the constipation so within a day or so I am back to normal.

In the first few months of being on the TKI, I spent a weekend in intense joint pain. When I was finally able to reach my oncology nurse practitioner on Tuesday, I was told that I could take over the counter pain relievers. It was at this point that I told her a few things - the first is that I had called and left a message on Monday, and no one called me. Then I had to call again on Tuesday in intense pain only to be told OTC medication was the solution. Second, OTC meds are NOT a long-term solution. I told her that if the pain continued, I would absolutely stop taking the medication and live my best life until I died.

I tend to exaggerate, anyone who knows me, knows I can get worked up about topics for which I am passionate. This was not an exaggeration, and neither was my pain. It was unbearable for days on end and the OTC medication barely touched the pain. My husband and my nurse were of course not happy to hear me say this, but the reality was that was the only part of my life that I could control at that time. It wasn't long after this that I talked to my Naturopathic team and got started on a pain management protocol in conjunction with the oncologist-approved medical marijuana. I felt more in control of my medical care at this point.

We don't get to ring the bell. Many of us do not get to stop treatment and 40-60% of those that do, experience a relapse within a few years. Most, if not all, of us don't look like what one thinks of when they think of a cancer patient. We may have thinning hair, but we are not bald. We aren't wearing scarves on our heads. We look fairly healthy but, on the inside, it may be a different story, especially for patients who are new to taking TKIs or switch medications.

Listen to your body. Think about the kind of care that you want, that works for YOU, and find a medical team that fits what you need. Palliative care and side effect management is really up to you, as the patient. No one should suffer, whether they have CML or another diagnosis. Advocate for yourself and if you can't, find someone who will be your voice.

SOURCES

The following printed materials were mentioned in this Chapter, and some additional resources (used with permission where possible, for reference only).

Palliative Care - https://www.webmd.com/palliative-care/what-is-palliative-care

Side Effects of Gleevec/Imatinib https://www.us.gleevec.com/side-effects/understanding-side-effects/

Who is Your
Support System?

Friends and Family First

As Eddie and I navigated finding the best medical team to treat me and CML, we also focused on friends and family. How do we relay what is happening without alienating people? We felt an announcement on social media wasn't an appropriate way to announce the news. We made a list and called our closest family and friends like we were volunteers at the public television telethon.

It was exhausting relaying the same information over and over…

Yes, I am going to be okay. It's manageable.

Chronic means there is no cure.

Life expectancy is the same if I take the pill at the same time every day, no exceptions.

I just need to get a bone marrow biopsy and CAT scan and then I can start the pill.

We don't know why this happened.

Yes, we're lucky they caught it early on routine bloodwork.

Yes, there are too many cancer cells in my body and it's scary to think about for too long.

I probably won't lose my hair. It might even go back to its pre-gray brunette.

Yes, there are side effects, but the doctor said her patients don't get severe symptoms.

Yes, for the rest of my life I have to take this pill unless there is a better option or a cure.

I could say all of these things and for a few days I even fooled myself. It was like I was reporting the news and not that it was happening to me.

Then it hit me.

I have cancer.

No one had actually said that to me.

The oncologist said, "You have leukemia. It's called Chronic Myeloid Leukemia or CML…"

She went on to explain…

I don't even know what. I think my mind went blank.

A STRONG DOSE OF REALITY

The reality was that I had cancer, and still do today.

There is no cure for CML.

I have it until there is a better option or a cure.

The words echoed in my head.

I cried in the shower.

I cried myself to sleep.

I cried for the life I had before diagnosis.

I cried for my mother who lost her 22 month battle with breast cancer in 1995 at the age of 46 years old.

I cried. Not like at the end of a sad movie but the kind of crying when someone you love dies. The kind that shakes your whole body and wears you down. I did it alone in the shower and I wondered if my mother had done the same when she was diagnosed.

I cried because my father again had someone in his life with cancer.

I cried for my four month old marriage.

I cried for all the people who die from cancer and never have the outcome that many CML patients have – to live a normal lifespan.

When the crying subsided, I did what I've always done. I pulled myself up by my bootstraps and got to work. Eddie and I focused on what we could control. We focused on making me comfortable so that my body could heal. We focused on laughing at least one time every day, a prescription from my naturopathic team. We focused on finding tools for remembering to take my medication and supplements.

And I called the women I knew would support me through anything – Team Sisters with Blisters.

In 2004 and 2005, we walked 60 miles in three days and raised money for breast cancer awareness and research. They were women I met during training walks, women with whom I was working, and their mothers and friends. We walked at least 10-15 miles on Saturdays and Sundays, with smaller groups and shorter walks during the week.

After spending hours together, we learned a lot about each other. We knew whose kids were struggling in school, whose significant other was supportive, whose husband couldn't function without his wife, and whose roommate dressed the dog in a team shirt and brought him to see us walking. And we got blisters.

We became Sisters with Blisters, complete with a sign that we carried, and branded logo and t-shirts. We wrote the names of our loved ones that we had lost to cancer on our shirts. We pinned ribbons on our backpacks representing the people we remembered and honored as we walked. We told stories about each of them.

Never in my wildest imagination did I think I would become one of the people with cancer, but it happened. Of course, I called my Sisters with Blisters who immediately jumped into action, as we had always done.

One went to healing services with us at church. She placed her warm hands on me as the congregation prayed. We didn't even know what we were praying about for me yet but we prayed. She and her husband brought us meals, helped us laugh everyday, and drove us when we didn't have the energy to drive ourselves.

Another "sister" asked me to meet her on a layover at the airport. She wanted to know if it was breast cancer. She was relieved when I told her no but was sad when I said we didn't know what it was yet. She bought dinner and wine. We talked about the what ifs and how she could support me. When I left, she gave me a tight hug.

THE ROCKS YOU TURN TO

My husband Eddie was, and remains, my rock. He supports me in ways I didn't even know I needed support. He hugs me without prompting just when I need it most. He holds my hand at blood draws and oncologist appointments. He drives me to and from my infusions. He tucks me in for naps. He listens to me. I couldn't be on this journey without him.

Over the years, we've talked about what palliative care is and what we would do if my CML took a turn for the worse. These are important conversations to have with loved ones. They need to know what we want so that they can make decisions if we cannot.

- Communicate with loved ones. They need you to talk to them about your CML as much as you need to be heard.

- Get Medical Directives completed. That's the HIPAA release, Health Care Power of Attorney, and Living Will.

- Be clear with yourself and others about what you want.

Not Everyone Belongs on Your Bus

As we moved along this path, Eddie and I realized there were people in our lives that were causing more stress than they were helping. Stress is bad for cancer and for overall health. When one friend stressed me out too much, my CML went from undetectable to slightly detectable. While I know that can happen as part of CML, I also know stress can be the cause. Knowing the level of stress I was experiencing, I chose to distance myself from that friend and others. We needed to be surrounded by love.

One of the friends I called to tell the news, one of the telethon calls, has barely spoken to me since. Am I hurt? Yes. Does it matter? Not really. I don't have the time or inclination to fight for relationships, especially if it is clear the other person doesn't want to put in the effort. Part of it is my age I think and part of it is that I fight cancer every single day and don't have the energy for challenging relationships. I have to protect my health, physical and mental.

Know Your Inner Circle

When I called the Sisters with Blisters, they rose to the occasion. That's the difference between those who are on your bus and in your circle, and the support you need. Find them; they could be people you already know, or people you'll meet along your journey.

I called my friends, Sisters with Blisters, who had walked 60 miles in three days with me back in 2004 and 2005 to raise money and awareness for breast cancer research. One of them thought I had breast cancer. While she was relieved it wasn't, she became what she always is in a crisis, the big sister. She said to sign her up for whatever I needed and send her a t-shirt in the color we wore for my cancer.

She, and the rest of the old team, were ready for a battle.

The TFR Decision:
Treatment Free or Stay the Course

"Treatment-free Remission (TFR) is achieved when a patient who has discontinued TKI therapy maintains a Deep Molecular Response (DMR) and does not need to restart treatment" (See Sources).

By far the most asked question I get is, "How long do you have to take the chemo pill?"

My answer is always the same, "Until there is a better option or until there is a cure."

That's not the case for all CML patients. Some are able to stop taking their TKI and remain in remission while 40-60% of others relapse within the first two years.

In December 2017, pharmaceutical company Novartis, the maker of Gleevec, announced that its other CML drug, Tasigna, was the first FDA Approved drug for TFR. That meant that patients who experienced deep molecular response (undetectable leukemia) for a consistent period of time were eligible to come off the drug. *As of the publication of this book, there is no other CML drug included in the FDA approval for TFR.* However, there are patients on other TKIs that stop taking their medication. Some do this without doctor approval and oversight while others are under their doctor's care as I've learned from social media groups for CML patients.

Honestly, the TFR debate is one of the reasons I am writing this book. It seems there is a lot of misinformation about the goal of taking a TKI.

This class of drugs was designed to manage CML, and were not intended as a cure.

A dear friend of mine made the decision to go off her chemo pill, with the guidance of her oncologist, and shared her experience:

> "For me personally, we contemplated this decision for close to three years. Everyone's situation is different given age, other health factors, the time it took to achieve an undetectable response, etc., and it's equally important to take these factors into account.
>
> It was truly the scariest decision we have ever made, and no one tells you how the decision will rock your world indefinitely. For me, will I ever be able to stop worrying about the cancer coming back? With routine blood draws every four months, the thought of my CML rearing its ugly head is always on my mind. I still can't decide if taking a chemo pill every day was scarier or if living in a constant state of fear is. And no one can possibly prepare you for this feeling. Yes, I was given every reassurance by my oncologist, I've had perfect blood draws for three years, but the *what if* is a lingering and constant fear."

Whether under the care of a doctor or not, TKIs, with the exception of Tasigna, are not approved for TFR. As my oncologist nurse practitioner has told me many times, these drugs were not designed for patients to stop taking them. Researchers are still learning about CML, most notably why 50% of patients fail out of TFR and end up on another TKI within a few years of stopping.

Furthermore, coming off TKIs should be done under the care of a doctor. Patients report coming off the drug and not knowing there are side effects of doing so. It's the same as what many of us experience when we first start taking the drug, sometimes worse. In fact, the TFR page for Tasigna specifically says patients may experience worse pain going off the drug than going on! These include muscle pain, arm and leg pain, joint and bone pain.

Oncologist and CML Researcher Dr. Kendra Sweet of H. Lee Moffitt Cancer Center in Tampa, said the following in an interview about TFR and side effects:

> *"TKI withdrawal syndrome is absolutely a real thing. Why does it happen? I don't really know. It may have something to do with something called KIT expression, but at the end of the day whatever causes it, it is real. And, it happens in about 25 to 30% of people when they discontinue their TKI. Usually it starts in, you know, maybe month one or two. And, on average lasts 6 months or so. Some people it's much less, some people it's longer. And usually, it's just kind of this low grade musculoskeletal pain, that's kind of diffuse. And usually, it's not something that prohibits people from their daily activities, but it's just there and it's frustrating. Can often be treated with ibuprofen or, you know, other anti-inflammatories. Some people find benefit in taking Claritin®, the allergy medication. Very infrequently do we need to give somebody steroids for a short period of time, but it does go away. And, what we don't want to do is restart a TKI just because of TKI withdrawal. Because it will go away. And again, it's usually fairly low grade. But, definitely don't let anyone tell you it's not real, because it's definitely a real thing"*

WHY DON'T I STOP TAKING THE CHEMO PILL?

The short answer is that it just isn't time.

My oncology team stands firmly on the conservative side of treatment, as do Eddie and I. Gleevec is working for me. My blood counts are normal and CML is undetectable. Side effects, which I explored more in an earlier chapter, are well-managed. There is no reason, clinical or otherwise, for me to stop taking the drugs.

My cancer is undetectable and while that was the goal, it doesn't happen for every patient. My BCR-ABL, leukemia cell count, lingered below 1% but not quite zero and fluctuated for a few months, if not a year, before reaching undetectable. Then it jumped up slightly for a couple months before becoming undetectable again.

I spent the better part of my first year on Gleevec in horrible pain. With the odds only being 50% that the leukemia would remain undetectable off the drug, I don't want to have to start on a TKI again. It was that bad.

While I meet the criteria, in terms of my CML being in deep molecular response, my oncologist, husband, and I agree there is still too much of a risk. Research for additional options is promising enough that I can wait a bit longer. My CML was growing fast for a "slow-growth" cancer; I've verified this with my oncologist several times, and that, for me, makes the risk too great.

There is a lot of research happening now that will impact CML patients. The UCLA and other research surrounding the eradication of CML stem cells is revolutionary. It would effectively be a cure for CML patients, and likely other cancer patients too. If given the chance, I would be a patient for the clinical trial.

There are patients who have severe side effects or other conditions that make it necessary to at least try TFR. The reality is that the original purpose of the TKIs was to manage CML, which it does, and not to come off the drug. Other CML patients make different decisions and I respect them for that. It's just not for me at this time.

Sources

The following printed materials were mentioned in this Chapter, and some additional resources (used with permission where possible, for reference only).

Treatment Free Remission - https://www.cmladvocates.net/tfr-cml-patients

Leukemia Lymphoma Society - TFR https://www.lls.org/sites/default/files/National/USA/Pdf/Publications/FS34_Treatment_Free_Remission2018.pdf

Novartis - Tasigna - TFR
https://www.us.tasigna.com/about-tasigna/treatment-free-remission-cml/

2017 Announcement of FDA approval for use and TFR
https://www.novartis.com/news/media-releases/novartis-drug-tasigna-approved-fda-first-and-only-cml-therapy-treatment-free-remission-data-its-label

Dr. Kendra Sweet discusses TFR
https://www.onclive.com/view/dr-sweet-discusses-tki-discontinuation-in-cml

Advocacy and Action

My husband Eddie and I have embraced partnerships with various foundations and causes. Even before my diagnosis, we discussed that our family supports causes related to health and education. It is part of who we are as individuals, as a couple, and as a family.

Advocacy and action were already part of who we are, so it was in our blood, so to speak, to embrace community through my CML journey.

To us, advocacy means giving back to the community in whatever way we can.

Supporting Cancer Patients

Through our journey as a couple and through our CML journey together, it is these connections that keep us moving forward. People genuinely care about us. When our friend created a Meal Train soon after I was diagnosed, we embraced the help and paid it forward when another friend was diagnosed with cancer.

The Leukemia and Lymphoma Society is a great resource. We formed Team McLopez with our family and friends, educated the community about blood cancer, and raised nearly $40,000 in four years for blood cancer research (see Sources).

Our friends held fundraisers across the country and online. They created a team t-shirt. They hosted raffles and painting parties. Our friends who own a bar had one of their distributors donate kegs of beer. A portion of the proceeds was donated to our team. It was also a time for me to connect with other CML patients.

CONNECTING WITH OTHER CML PATIENTS

My father's college friend's son has CML and is thriving. He runs marathons and is a patient advocate with LLS for those newly diagnosed. He was the first CML patient I met, and he offered advice and support. He said he takes his chemo pill every evening with dinner, so he doesn't forget and because he does better on a full stomach. I've taken my chemo pill this way from the start of treatment, because of his recommendation.

The DJ at Light the Night is a CML patient and neuroscientist who sees a well-known CML Specialist in the area.

His first question was, "What are your counts and which TKI are you taking?"

This is a common mantra from CML patients, in my experience. I think it comes from a shared experience that is different from other cancer patients.

There is the longest diagnosed CML patient in Arizona who loves showing off his three sons, including a set of twins. He thought CML would stop him from having biological children and it didn't.

I received a call from a mother whose grown daughter had been recently diagnosed. The daughter's husband had divorced her and left her with two kids. They were all living with the mother and weren't sure what to ask doctors and where to find support. I offered what I knew from my experience and got them involved with LLS.

There was the quiet guy handing Survivor t-shirts at Light the Night who let me get a photo with him. I want to remember the faces so I can pray for all of us.

There was me fangirling on a motorcycle racer who has Acute Lymphoblastic Leukemia (ALL) with the same mutation as me. It is somewhat rare for ALL but it happens. I said, "Hey, can we get a photo together. We're the only two in the room with this mutation." It was weird but he looked at me and understood that cancer patients all unite at some level, weird or not.

There is my now dear, young friend, who was diagnosed with CML in her early twenties as she was finishing college. She was like me in the sense that she thought she was tired from a busy life but a visit to the ER told her otherwise. She is now thriving and going to law school.

Another friend was introduced to me through Facebook. She is a breast cancer survivor who has CML as a secondary cancer. She is on Medicare and advocates for patient rights to accessible and affordable treatment and medication.

There is the Founder of Families Raising Hope who is a TFR CML patient. She and her husband, along with another couple, run their nonprofit and raise funds for Arizona families who have a member with cancer.

I advocate for all of them and for all of you. It was a blessing to meet others who were at different points in their CML journey.

We are a community.

SHARING MY STORY

Through our time with LLS, I told my story. I've spoken at locations across the Phoenix area and on the main stage at Light the Night as Honored Hero in 2017. My story is on the national LLS website Inspirational Stories (see Sources). I felt it was important to share my CML story because CML is different from other cancers.

We don't sit at infusion centers getting our chemo.

We don't lose our hair.

And we don't get to ring the bell.

FAMILIES RAISING HOPE

When our family needed financial support during the pandemic, we turned to a local organization called Families Raising Hope. I spoke to Melissa, one of the Founders, and learned she is also a CML patient. I am pretty sure this means we're bonded for life!

In a time of need, Families Raising Hope provided our family a grant to aid with living expenses and the cost of my chemo pill.

Melissa and I have since taken each other under our wings as support and to simply know there's a CML patient available when we need to chat. We even appeared on Phoenix Business Radio X together to support Families Raising Hope.

Eddie and I have since participated in events with Families Raising Hope (see Sources) and will continue to do so. Now that I feel better, we want to support organizations that have supported us. We believe in paying it forward when we can, however we can.

CHILDREN'S LEUKEMIA RESEARCH ASSOCIATION (CLRA)

Another foundation that helped us when we needed it most was the Children's Leukemia Research Association. Located in New York, they support children and adults with cancer expenses including living expenses and the cost of medication.

From the CLRA Facebook page, "In the early 2000s, many of our fellow blood cancer support organizations stopped providing financial assistance to patients. Our Patient Aid Program was created to help fulfill that growing need."

At the time of this publication, there was a cap on the dollar amount per family, so if you are in need, check their website, call, and/or apply for assistance. The team is friendly, informative, and willing to help (see Sources).

Affordable Access to Medication

I actually found CLRA as I was researching resources to help pay for my chemo pill. Depending on the insurance we had, the out of pocket cost for my Gleevec prescription was $50-$300 per month. The retail price for my prescription is $13,500 per month or $162,000 per year. That's the cost of a house in some areas!

I understand from other patients, $50-$300 per month is on the lower end of copay costs, with some insurance companies not even covering the drug prescribed by their oncologist. Even on good insurance that offers coverage for TKIs, there are annual changes so from one year to the next, we don't know what is covered and how much it will cost.

The Cost of Cancer

The money stress from the cost of cancer is enough to make you sicker. With the insurance that I've had since my diagnosis, the challenges have included:

- Copay amount changes year to year

- Brand name vs. Generic coverage

- Bureaucracy and lack of customer service at Specialty Pharmacies

MY TAKE

Here's my take on each of these issues, from my personal experience. CML patients need our TKI monthly in order to stay alive.

I'll say that again for the politicians, big pharma, and those of you sitting in the back:

CML patients need our TKI monthly in order to stay alive.

There is no reason why this class of drugs shouldn't be covered by every health insurance company. We need our TKI to survive. Here's what I think:

- No patient should ever have to say to a pharmacy or delivery service that if they don't get me my meds, my cancer will grow.

- I should never have to say that I will sue a company because my cancer is growing as a result of their lack of competence.

- I should not be put on hold for upwards of two hours to refill a prescription.

- I should not have to ask a delivery service how many packages their driver went out with and how many he reported. (He went out with 10 and only delivered nine. Mine was stuck in his truck. They were delivered by 5AM because I trolled them on Twitter all night.)

- I should not be required to call the FDA to ask how my medication is legally allowed to be dispensed in order to convince a Specialty Pharmacy that we can update a prescription.

- I should not be charged two copays because the Specialty Pharmacy system can't charge as one even though my oncologist only submitted one prescription.

- I should not have to have my oncologist rewrite my prescription because of issues with the Specialty Pharmacy.

- I should not have to find out the manufacturer supply chain in order to get my medication refilled.

- I should not be the one dictating which manufacturer a Specialty Pharmacy has in stock so that patients can get best copay assistance.

- I shouldn't be doing research for pharmacy managers.

- I shouldn't need to call my Senators and Congresspeople to get my chemo medication.

- I shouldn't have multiple grievances with my health care plan and their pharmacies.

- I shouldn't be told that a prescription can be filled at a local pharmacy when it needs to be from a Specialty Pharmacy.

- My state health insurance shouldn't cancel coverage of my life saving medication.

All of these scenarios are real events that have happened to me. Just me. I am one cancer patient. I cannot imagine what the rest of you have been through.

That all being said, here is what I recommend for you if you are having challenges with affordable access to your TKI:

- Ask at the oncologist's office if there is a patient advocate and/or social worker.

- Ask your insurance if they offer someone to assist you.

- Call your Senators and Congresspeople.

- File a grievance against your insurance company.

- Record your phone calls. When they pick up and say they are recording, tell them you are as well. They are a lot more helpful.

- Ask if your oncologist can write the prescription differently to get a better copay. (I went from two copays to one simply by asking for 100 mg. pills instead of 400 mg + 100 mg for my 500 mg. prescription of Gleevec.)

- Ask if you can get an override for the brand name to get coverage.

- Ask if you can be covered if you use the generic brand.

Each pharmacy has different programs and there may be copay assistance. They don't always tell patients about the assistance. Your doctor's office may be able to help as well. Keep on them, all of them.

SUPPORTING STUDENTS

As I began to feel better, I no longer wanted to be a cancer patient. As I've written about in this book, I wanted to be ME. Eddie and I decided to end our time with our local LLS chapter and find other ways to support the community.

When we were early in our relationship, Eddie invited me to an event at his Alma Mater. It was fun to see him work the room. He introduced me to people that he knew I'd like – the lawyer from New Jersey, the spouses of alums, and the students, all of whom were, and are, gifts to us. We joke that we meet 100% of the people at events; he meets 80% and I meet 20% of them. I find my favorites and get comfortable!

I've also reconnected with my Alma Mater, making videos for students in writing courses and speaking to Liberal Arts majors about my career. I've shared my CML diagnosis as a way to connect with students and let them know they can accomplish anything, even when setbacks occur.

It's this type of connection that is not only a pillar of our family, but support. When the pandemic happened, we had a full social life of

Zoom events. We still had our community. It was a blessing for sure!

Find the people and organizations to support you wherever you are in your journey. When you can and if you can, give back. I promise it will be good for you and your community.

SOURCES

The following printed materials were mentioned in this Chapter, and some additional resources (used with permission where possible, for reference only).

Team McLopez - https://www.lls.org/leukemia/chronic-myeloid-leukemia

LLS Inspirational Stories - https://www.lls.org/story/anne

Phoenix Business RadioX talking about Families Raising Hope and sharing our stories - https://businessradiox.com/podcast/phoenixbusinessradio/anne-mcauley-lopez-with-agency-content-writer-and-melissa-kovalesky-with-families-raising-hope/)

Families Raising Hope - https://www.familiesraisinghope.org/

Children's Leukemia Research Association - https://www.facebook.com/ChildrensLeukemiaResearchAssociation/

Conclusion

After listening to Dr. Sweet's webinar about the importance of exercise for CML patients to fight fatigue, I began focusing on taking small steps.

Like with other chronic illnesses, it seems the days of strength and days of fatigue are challenging, if impossible, to predict, so we take our small steps and big steps one day at a time.

On a particularly trying day, I was on the treadmill having a conversation with God and my mother about why my body wasn't cooperating. The leukemia had become detectable again, and I felt defeated.

Then Rachel Platten's **Fight Song** came on through my headphones:

> *This is my fight song*
>
> *Take back my life song*
>
> *Prove I'm alright song*
>
> *My power's turned on*
>
> *Starting right now I'll be strong*
>
> *I'll play my fight song*
>
> *And I don't really care if nobody else believes*
>
> *'Cause I've still got a lot of fight left in me*

It was at this moment that I took back my life.

I could feel my mother's hand on my back. We were not giving up. I have cancer but cancer doesn't have me. I stood taller and walked faster. And in that moment my body became stronger. I cried tears of victory.

This is my fight.	I am strong.
This is our fight.	You are strong.

Not soon after, I began to feel the inspiration to write this book. And my CML became undetectable again and has remained undetectable. The road may not be what we envisioned but we can embrace who we are and make the most of all that we have.

Eddie and I have always said that we choose hope. To that end, I have written this book of hope, not despair. I've written it for you and your families.

Keep fighting.

Additional Resources

I thought it important to include some great CML and general cancer or leukemia organizations that could provide information, resources, and guidance for you, your family, friends and associates:

The National CML Society - www.nationalcmlsociety.org

The Leukemia and Lymphoma Society - www.lls.org

Children's Leukemia Research Association (for adults too) - www.childrensleukemia.org

International Chronic Myeloid Leukemia Foundation - www.cml-foundation.org

The American Cancer Society - www.cancer.org

Cancer Support Community - www.cancersupportcommunity.org

About The Author

Anne McAuley Lopez is a professional content writer for business websites for small and medium-sized businesses. In September 2020, she launched Agency Content Writer which is focused on creating content for Digital Marketing Agencies. Specialties include writing for IT services, real estate, home services, travel, marketing, and legal service clients. Her work has been featured in Entrepreneur, Trendsetters, Arizona Republic, Elephant Journal, and Thrive Global. A graduate of the University of Connecticut with a BA in Economics, she fell in love with writing from an early age, and made her passion a business.